MISSION TO MARS

SCIENCE, ART, TECHNOLOGY & WRITING

240 Activities And Prompts

Sarah Janisse Brown

We use the Dyslexie Font by Christian Boer

The Thinking Tree Publishing Company, LLC

FUNSCHOOLINGBOOKS.COM

MISSION TO MARS

WAS CREATED IN COLLABORATION WITH SEVERAL ARTISTS, EDITORS & RESEARCHERS

Detailed Illustrations By: Sarah Brown

(Using MidJourney A. I. Art Technology)

Line Drawings & Mazes by: Antoinette Marlow—

Black & White Drawing By: Notika Pashenko

Comic Art By: Fabio Cordero

Research Prompts by: Luke Prail

Creative Writing Prompts: Fern Hood & Georgia McKibben

All About Mars By:

Matthew, Kristi & Brayden Skinner

Inspirations, Ideas & Resources By:

Katina Aleksander

Pam White

Amanda Goldman

Elyse Marie Haile

Elizabeth Fuqua

Arti Mahendra Sharma

Sarah Neel

Erica Horton

Becca Sue Olson Mueller

Diane C. Heeney

Sue Gerdes

Dennis Janisse

NAME:

DATE:

CONTACT INFO:

INTRODUCTION:

This book was created by homeschooling families who are interested in travel to Mars. We created this book to help our families, especially our children, to be able to envision what life might be like on our neighboring planet.

This book will get you thinking thoughts you have never thought before. You will be presented with challenges, problems, opportunities and questions without answers! You will need to do your own research to figure out how to survive and build safe homes and communities on Mars. If you are using this book, we are expecting you to step up and think like a leader, and be ready to tap into every bit of imagination and courage that you possess.

Moving to Mars is a big deal. You might die trying, or you might become the parent of the first baby born on the red planet! You might come up with ideas and solutions that have yet to enter the human mind. You are here to learn things that are still unknown. When it comes to moving to Mars, there are no experts. There are no people out there with personal experience! Yet a lot of people are working toward building communities off planet, and in your lifetime there is a good chance that people will step foot on Mars and make themselves at home. So let's get a head start and figure out what it's going to take to do the simplest things like breathe, eat, play, and access fresh water on another planet.

Tips:

Use two or three pages per weekday to make this book last an entire semester.

BUILD YOUR LIBRARY

Get a stack of books and magazines with information about Mars, technology, survival skills & space travel.

LIST YOUR BOOKS HERE:

_____

_____

_____

_____

_____

_____

LEARNING TOOLS

Websites for Research

_____

_____

_____

_____

https://mars.nasa.gov/

https://www.jpl.nasa.gov/missions/mars-pathfinder-sojourner-rover

https://spaceplace.nasa.gov/mars-rovers/en/

https://www.natgeokids.com/uk/discover/science/space/facts-about-mars/

https://nineplanets.org/kids/mars/

https://spaceplace.nasa.gov/all-about-mars/en/

https://www.ducksters.com/science/mars.php

https://en.wikipedia.org/wiki/History_of_Mars_observation

https://www.wondriumdaily.com/martian-seasons-climate-and-axial-tilt/

https://www.rocketstem.org/category/mars/

https://www.nature.com/articles/d41586-022-02968-2

https://mars.nasa.gov/resources/26995/perseverance-workspace-at-skinner-ridge/

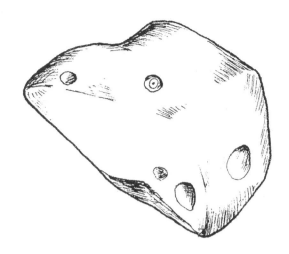

FUN FACTS ABOUT MARS:

1. Mars is home to Olympus Mons, the largest volcano in our solar system & is almost three times the height of Mt. Everest

2. Mars has two types of snow

3. Mars has four seasons like Earth, but the seasons vary in length

4. It would take more than six Mars planets to create the same size as Earth

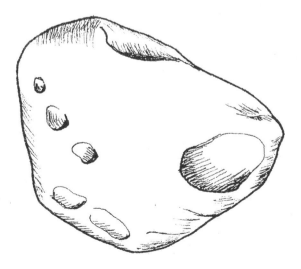

ALL ABOUT MARS

Before we start let's make sure we know the basics about Mars. It is the fourth planet from the sun. The planet Mars is named after the Roman god of war. It's about 142 million miles from the sun, which is 50 percent farther than the Earth is from the sun. Mars has an elliptical orbit of the sun that has gradually become more elongated over the past centuries.

The earliest records show that Mars was first observed as far back as the time of the ancient Egyptians. Chinese records show the movement of Mars in the sky back to 1054 BC. These observations were all done with just the eyes. It was in 1610 that Galileo Galilei made some of the first observations with the telescope. Galileo and other astronomers were able to see the tilt of the planet and its elliptical orbit when Mars was closest to the Earth. The telescope also allowed them to see the features on Mars, like hills and valleys.

Someday humans will make it to Mars, and when they do they will change the planet. Some visionaries dream of building cities for millions of people on the Red Planet. Would you move to Mars if you had the opportunity?

IMAGINE WHAT MARS WILL LOOK LIKE WITH CITIES!

TERRAIN:

Mars is commonly called the Red Planet because of its high content of iron in its soil. The iron rusts and produces the red color on its surface and in the atmosphere. Mars can have huge dust storms that can last for months and cover the entire planet. The atmosphere is 100 times thinner than Earths and it has very little oxygen. You would need a spacesuit to even go outside. The climate of Mars is considered very extreme with both deserts, polar ice caps, extinct volcanoes, and deep canyons.

Scientists and visionaries are working towards making Mars habitable. If that happens the terrain will change. Maybe someday the planet will have forests, farms, and cities!

Someday you may be on a mission to Mars. You may even move there and start a family! But this year your mission is one of imagination and research. The things you learn and invent now can determine what the future will be on the planet. Let's start by learning everything we can. And when we can't find answers, let's just use our imaginations.

IMAGINE HOMESCHOOLING ON MARS

ATMOSPHERE:

It would be very easy to get around since the gravity on Mars is very weak compared to Earth's. You could jump higher as you move around in the thin atmosphere. It is a terrestrial planet, meaning that its surface is very hard and rocky much like Earth's. Earth and Mars each have an atmosphere, a hydrosphere, a cryosphere, and a lithosphere. This means that like Earth, Mars also has air, water, ice and geology that all work together to make its environment.

While Earth has only one moon, Mars has two. They were discovered by American Astronomer Asaph Hall and are named Phobos and Deimos. They are both very small and have little to no effect on Mars. Phobos is a little under 14 miles (22.5 km) wide and Deimos is nearly 8 miles (12.9 Km) wide. The material makeup of these two moons appear similar to many asteroids in the outer asteroid belt and many scientists believe them to actually be captured asteroids.

In order for humans to live on Mars they will need to create alternate environments where humans and plants can survive and thrive. Let's imagine ways to make this happen. Anything is possible!

IMAGINE GROWING PLANTS ON MARS

CLIMATE/WEATHER:

The average temperature is -62 degrees Celsius which is almost -80 degrees Fahrenheit. Near the poles the temperature can drop to - 195 degrees F (-126C) where a summer day near the equator can get up to 70 degrees F (21 degrees C). The days on Mars are a little bit longer than on Earth. The days are 24.6 hours long. Even though the days are approximately the same, a year on Mars is 687 Earth days. Would you like having a birthday only once every two years?

There are two types of snow that fall on Mars - water ice and carbon dioxide (a.k.a. dry ice). Only the dry ice snow actually reaches the ground. Because it gets so cold on Mars, the water-ice snow evaporates into gas before reaching the ground.

Season changes can be detected by the movement of carbon dioxide falling to the surface as snow flakes and then back up into the atmosphere in gas form. As the seasons change there are dark streaks that appear in the Spring/Summer seasons and then tend to disappear with the Fall/Winter seasons. These streaks are the closest thing to water that has been discovered on the surface of Mars. Where there is water, there is potential for life!

IMAGINE WAYS TO ACCESS WATER ON MARS

MISSIONS:

When a spacecraft departs Earth, it is at a speed of about 24,600 mph (about 39,600 kph). The trip to Mars will take about seven months and about 300 million miles (480 million kilometers). NASA has sent several rovers to Mars and each had their own mission. The first one landed in 1997 and was called Sojourner. Its mission was just to move around taking pictures and recording measurements of the chemical makeup of the terrain and the atmosphere. The next ones landed in 2004, Spirit and Opportunity. Their sole mission was to find the existence of water on Mars. The next one, Curiosity, landed in August of 2012. It was looking to see if Mars had everything that life needed to exist; lasting water and the correct chemicals. The latest rover to date landed in February 2021, called Perseverance. Its mission is to see if there were any signs of life, past or present, and to see if humans could one day explore Mars. Many scientists think that Mars used to be a warmer, wetter place thousands of years ago and suffered a major flood. The current science goal NASA is working on for Mars is to "Seek Signs of Life."

As part of its research, the Perseverance Rover is drilling for samples on Mars to determine the chemical makeup and to see if there is evidence of ancient microbial life and the possibility of supporting life in the future.

One of these drill sites is called **Skinner Ridge**, a rock outcrop which is made of fine-grained sandstone similar to a type of rock seen in many places on Earth. This and other drill sites will be scattered with samples in sealed tubes that will be picked up by another mission in conjunction with **ESA** (European Space Agency) that will bring them back to Earth in the **2030**'s for more in-depth analysis.

IMAGINE WHAT IT WILL BE LIKE TO BUILD HOMES ON MARS

MISSIONS TO MARS

Would you like to travel to Mars?

Do you think that you would want to live there?

What will it take to support life
and build communities on the Red Planet?

Let's research,

explore,

imagine,

and get ready

to move to Mars!

The activities in this Fun-Schooling Journal will
help you to envision what life could be like in the
future on another planet!

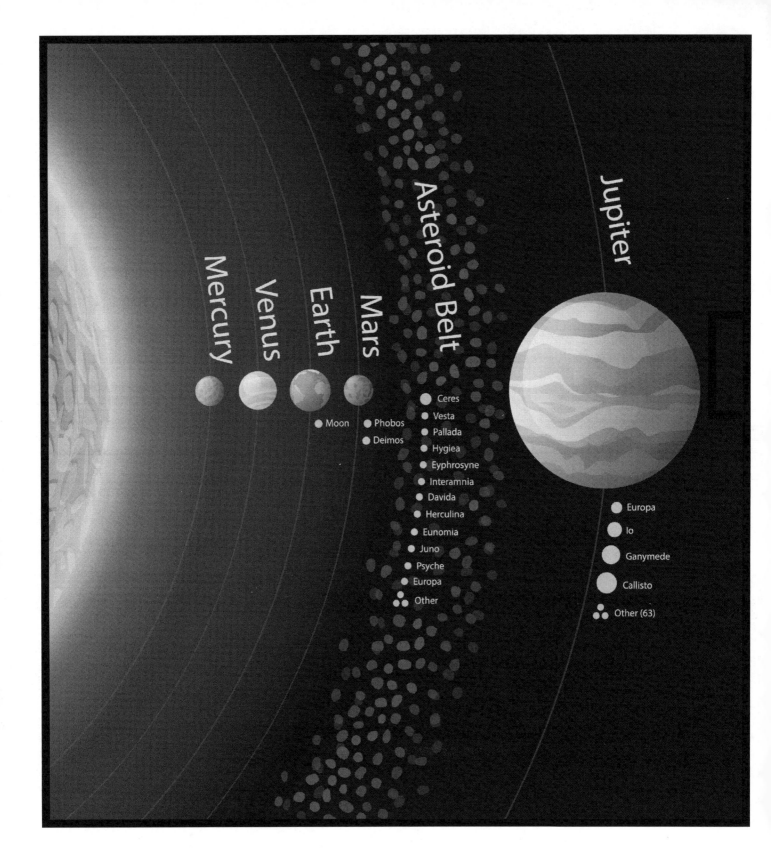

How far away is Mars from Earth?

_____

_____

_____

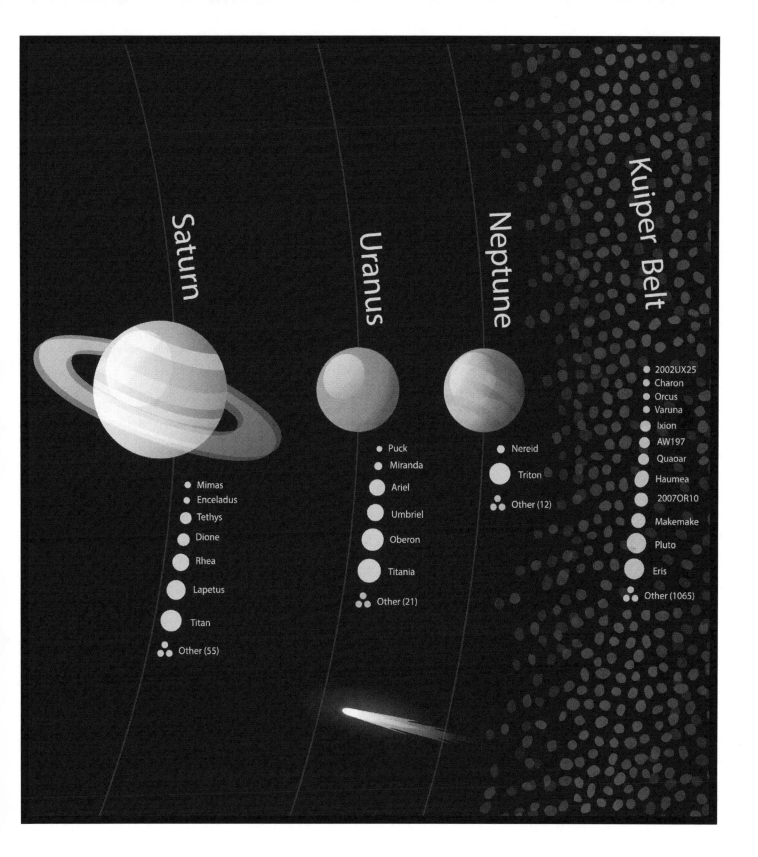

How long will it take to travel to Mars?

_____

_____

_____

TIMELINE OF SPACE EXPLORATION:

1900-1920:

_____

_____

1920-1940:

_____

_____

1940-1960:

_____

_____

1960-1980:

_____

_____

1980-2000:

_____

_____

2000-PRESENT:

_____

_____

SPELLING TIME

Choose a Letter: _____

Now search your books for 20 words that begin or end with this letter.

_____ _____

_____ _____

_____ _____

_____ _____

_____ _____

_____ _____

_____ _____

_____ _____

_____ _____

Use these words to create a silly story or poem about a day in your life on Mars.

_____

_____

_____

_____

_____

_____

_____

AN AWESOME QUOTE:

Who Said It:

_____

Copy the Quote Here:

_____
_____
_____
_____
_____
_____
_____

**TODAY
I WILL...**

IN TEN YEARS I PLAN TO...

NOTE TO FUTURE SELF:

_____
_____
_____

News from Mars

Month: Day: Year:

THE BEST UNDERGROUND CITIES

Life on the Red Planet

Month: Day: Year:

SMALL HOMES & BIG DREAMS

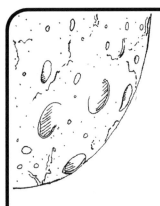

BE CREATIVE!

IMAGINE YOU ARE LEADING A MISSION TO MARS

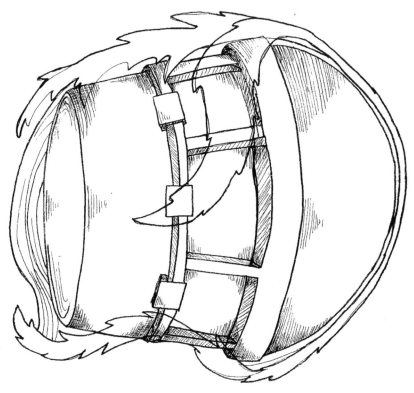

What kind of spacecraft would you use to reach Mars?
What materials would you choose for the spacecraft?
Explain below, and illustrate your ideas.

_____

_____

_____

_____

_____

_____

_____

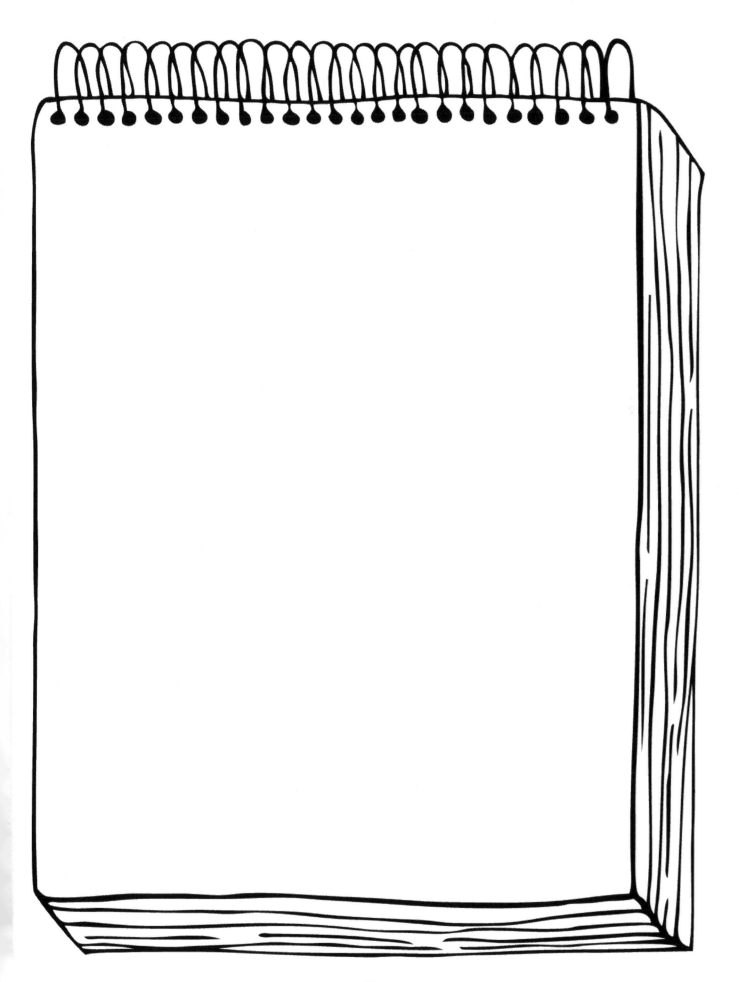

CREATIVE WRITING

Continue the story:

Rowan was so excited; the day was finally here!! He jumped out of bed and ran downstairs, joining his family as they crowded around the television. The news anchor said with excitement, "Now, across satellite links, for the first time in history, Commander James Strongbow is joining us live from Mars. Commander, welcome! Congratulations on a successful mission! Please, tell us about Mars so far."

A hazy pixelated image of the famous astronaut appeared on the screen, and he said...

_____
_____
_____
_____
_____
_____
_____
_____
_____
_____
_____
_____
_____
_____
_____
_____

_____
_____
_____
_____
_____
_____
_____
_____
_____
_____
_____
_____
_____
_____

Add some artwork:

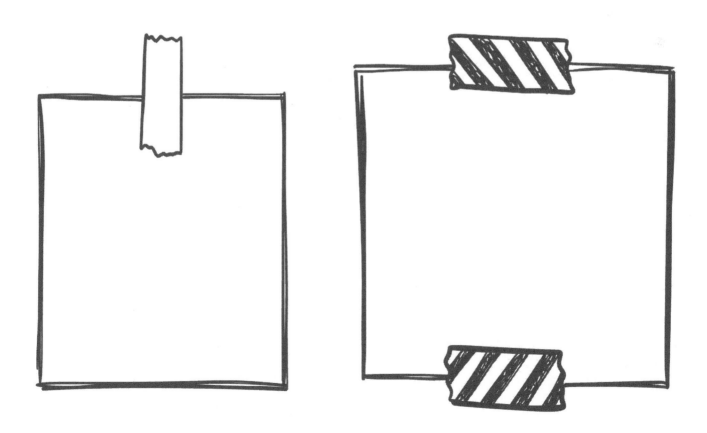

MISSION TO MARS SCRAPBOOK

While researching online take time to print out some pictures to stick to this page.

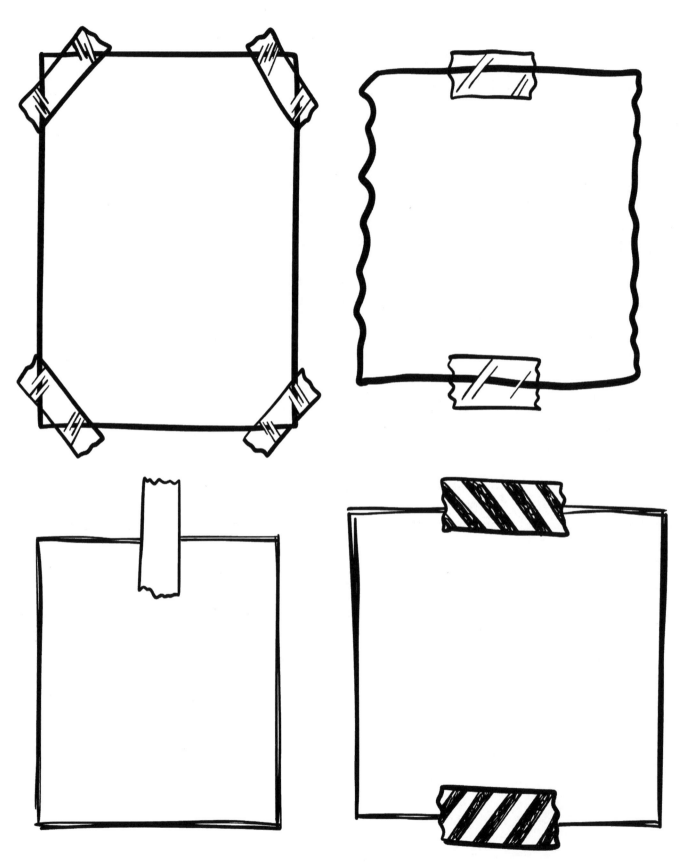

FIND A WAY THROUGH THE MAZE

SPACE TALK

albedo	aperture	asterism
Alpha Centauri	aphelion	asteroid
apastron	apogee	astronaut

Look up each word. Choose the most unfamiliar word from this list and write the definition here:

_____

_____

_____

_____

_____

_____

_____

Use this word in three sentences:

1._____

_____

2._____

_____

3._____

_____

News from Mars

Month: Day: Year:

FIRST HUG ON MARS

Life on the Red Planet

Month: Day: Year:

SIBLINGS HOMESCHOOL IN SPACE

CREATIVE WRITING

Continue the story:

Finally, after many long months journeying through space, Stargazer II had finally come to rest on the Red Planet. Astronauts Lydia, Evie, and Georgia waited patiently on board. Years of research, training and preparation had led to this moment. They held their breath as the safety checks were completed and then, after what seemed like an eternity, the all clear flashed green on the screen. They opened the doors, stepped outside and they could scarcely believe their eyes...

_____

_____

_____

_____

_____

_____

_____

_____

_____

_____

_____

_____

_____

_____

_____

_____

_____

Add some artwork:

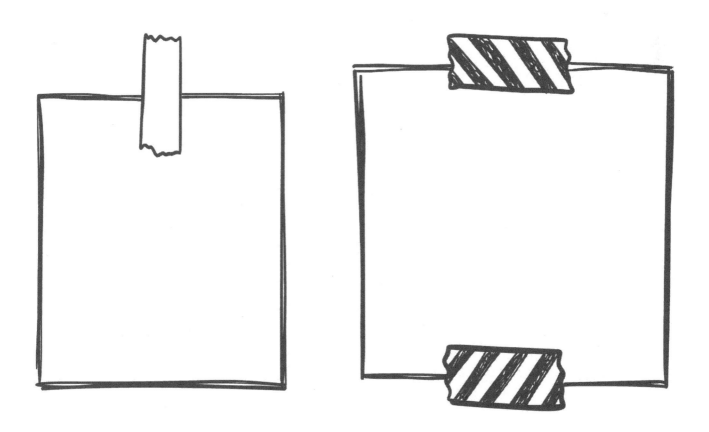

LISTENING TIME

Turn on a Podcast or News Show about Space or Technology

Notes:

_____

_____

_____

_____

_____

_____

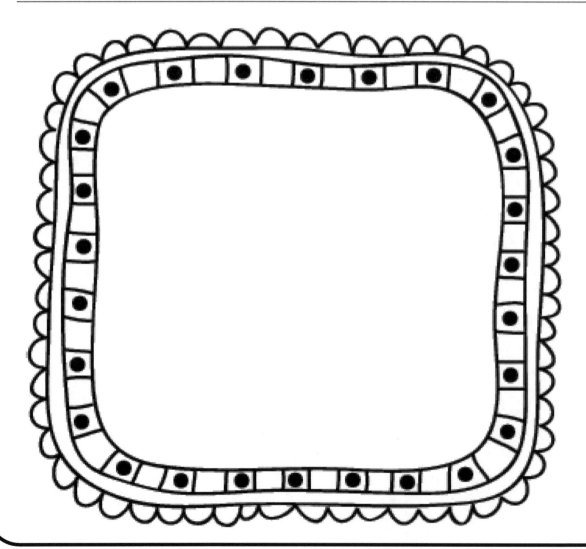

TRAVELING TO MARS

How will you spend your time? Draw your plans:

MISSION TO MARS SCRAPBOOK

While researching online take time to print out some pictures to stick to this page.

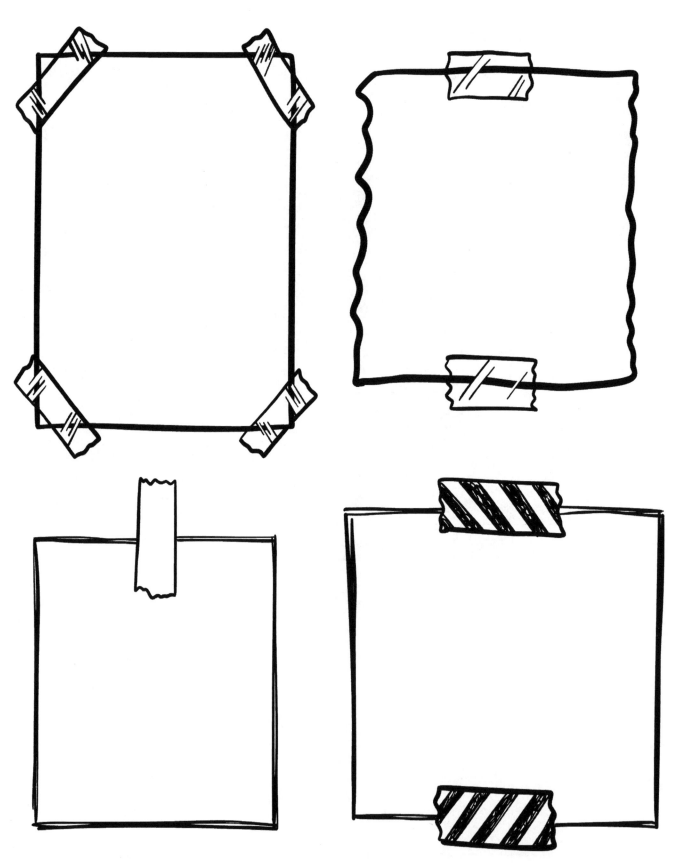

FIND A WAY THROUGH THE MAZE

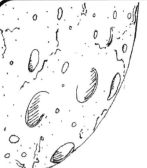

BE CREATIVE!

IMAGINE YOU ARE LEADING A MISSION TO MARS

Once you reach Mars, what would you like to research? What would be the first assignment for a science department of your team?

_____

_____

_____

_____

_____

_____

_____

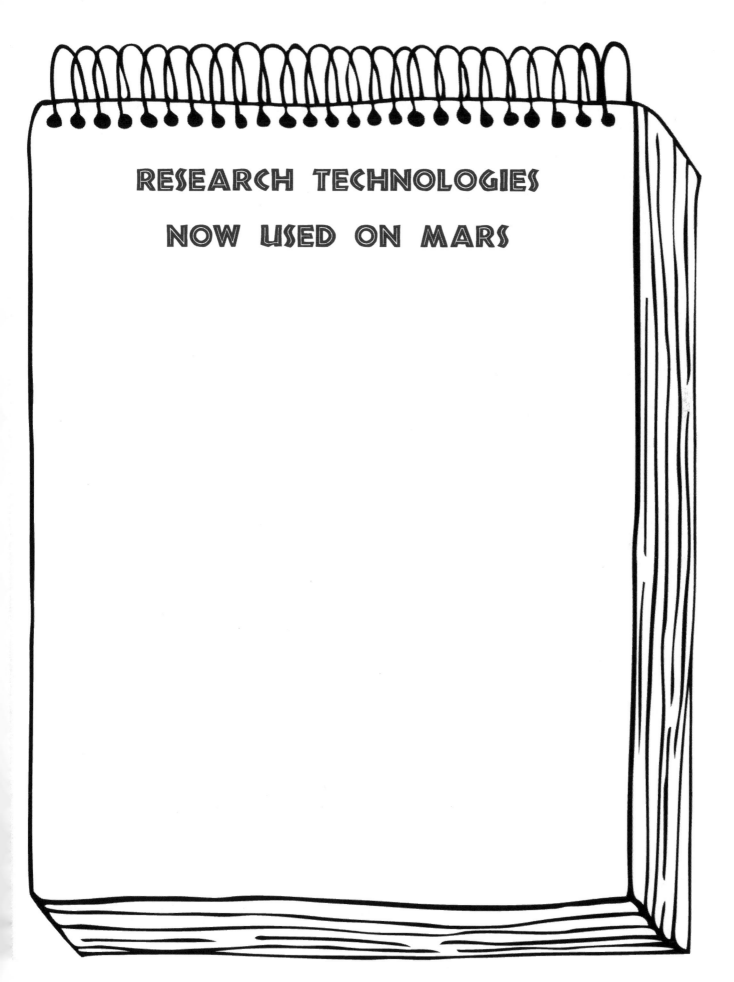

RESEARCH TECHNOLOGIES

NOW USED ON MARS

News from Mars

Month: Day: Year:

ENCLOSED PARKS BOAST REAL GRASS!

Life on the Red Planet

Month: Day: Year:

MAR'S MOST INTRIGUING GREENHOUSE

What is the closest distance from Mars to Earth?
What is the farthest? Why are there changes in the
distance?

_____

_____

_____

_____

_____

_____

_____

_____

Write down three facts about the orbit of Mars:

1._____

_____

2._____

_____

3._____

_____

SPELLING TIME

Choose a Letter: _____

Now search your books for **20** words that
begin or end with this letter.

_____   _____
_____   _____
_____   _____
_____   _____
_____   _____
_____   _____
_____   _____
_____   _____
_____   _____
_____   _____

Use these words to create a silly story or
poem about a day in your life on Mars.

_____
_____
_____
_____
_____
_____
_____
_____
_____

CREATIVE WRITING

Continue the story:

"Mars-expo III to base, come in! Come in! Do you read me?" Silence answered.

"I repeat, Mars-expo III to base, come in! Come in! Do you read me?"

Again, nothing. Lachlan knew they had drifted off course and no one could hear them.

"What do we do, Commander?" asked Kaleb.

Remembering his training, Lachlan took a deep breath, opened his manual, and began to push buttons on the screen. What happened next changed everything...

_____

_____

_____

_____

_____

_____

_____

_____

_____

_____

_____

_____

_____

_____

_____

_____

_____

_____

_____

_____

_____

_____

_____

_____

_____

_____

_____

_____

_____

Add some artwork:

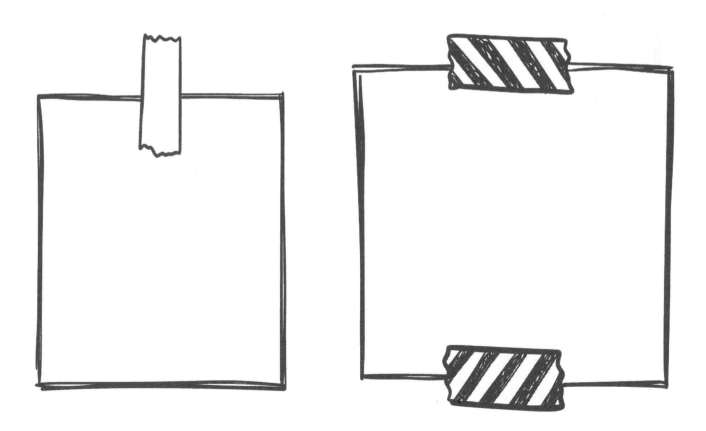

SPACE TALK

background radiation	black body	celestial
Bailey's beads	black hole	celestial equator
binary star	bolometer	cislunar

Look up each word. Choose the most unfamiliar word from this list and write the definition here:

_____

_____

_____

_____

_____

_____

_____

Use this word in three sentences:

1._____

_____

2._____

_____

3._____

_____

News from Mars

Month: Day: Year:

MARS-BURGER RESTAURANT NOW OPEN!

Life on the Red Planet

Month: Day: Year:

WARMER PLANET BURSTS TO LIFE

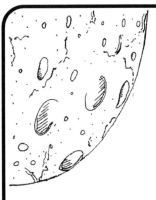

BE CREATIVE!

IMAGINE YOU ARE LEADING A MISSION TO MARS

What food would you take from Earth for your mission?
What food do you plan to grow in your Mars settlement?

_____

_____

_____

_____

_____

_____

DESIGN, INVENT, BUILD & PLAY

Use Lego, Clay, Art Supplies or Digital Art Apps to build
a model of your created environment on Mars.

MISSION TO MARS SCRAPBOOK

While researching online take time to print out some pictures to stick to this page.

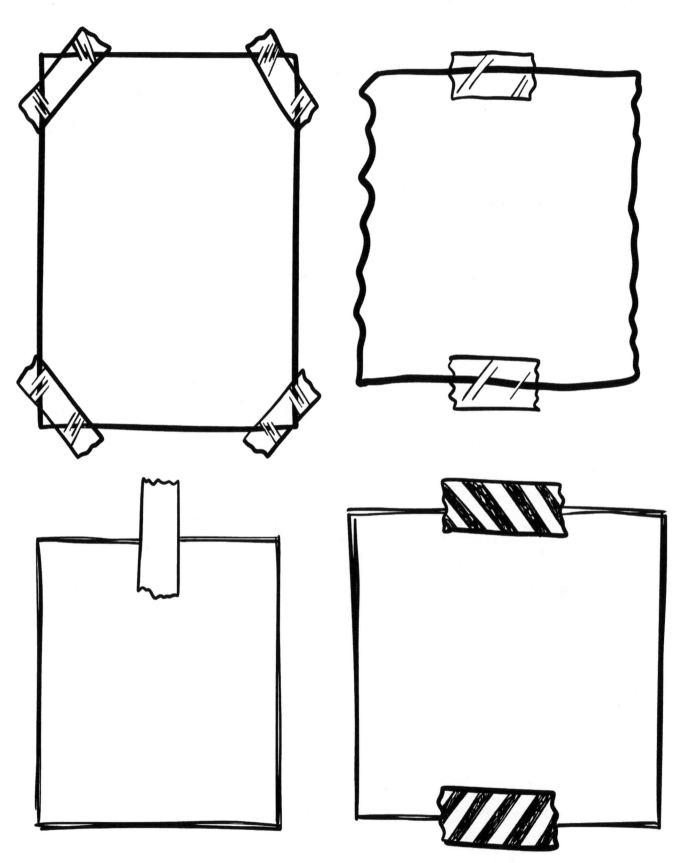

FIND A WAY THROUGH THE MAZE

SPACE TALK

cosmic rays	cosmos	dark matter
cosmology	crater	declination
cosmonaut	crescent moon	deep space

Look up each word. Choose the most unfamiliar word from this list and write the definition here:

_____

_____

_____

_____

_____

_____

_____

Use this word in three sentences:

1._____

_____

2._____

_____

3._____

_____

SPELLING TIME

Choose a Letter: _____

Now search your books for **20** words that
begin or end with this letter.

_____   _____
_____   _____
_____   _____
_____   _____
_____   _____
_____   _____
_____   _____
_____   _____
_____   _____
_____   _____

Use these words to create a silly story or
poem about a day in your life on Mars.

_____
_____
_____
_____
_____
_____
_____
_____

AN AWESOME QUOTE:

Who Said It:

_____

Copy the Quote Here:

_____
_____
_____
_____
_____
_____
_____

**TODAY
I WILL...**

IN TEN YEARS I PLAN TO...

NOTE TO FUTURE SELF:

_____
_____
_____

Issue #

News from Mars

Month: Day: Year:

MAYOR SPENDS ENTIRE BUDGET ON
ARTIFICIAL PLANTS & TREES TO BOOST MORALE

Life on the Red Planet

Month: Day: Year:

EARTHY BILLIONAIRE BUILDS "MARS MANSION" FOR GROWING FAMILY

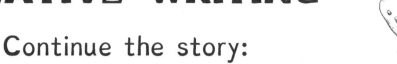

CREATIVE WRITING

Continue the story:

Indiana checked their logs and their food supplies. After 2 months on Mars, their provisions were running low and would soon reach critical levels. The Veg-01 they had built was working well and the plants were growing but they wouldn't be ready in time. They had to find food. She called a meeting with the rest of the crew.

"It's time", she said, "We have to send out a team to forage for food. Do I have any volunteers?"

"I'll go," said Knox.

"And I will go too," said Malachi.

They prepared their vehicle and their protective suits, and at first light they set out. It wasn't long before they encountered....

_____

_____

_____

_____

_____

_____

_____

_____

_____

_____

_____

_____

_____

_____

_____

_____

_____
_____
_____
_____
_____
_____
_____
_____
_____
_____
_____
_____
_____

Add some artwork:

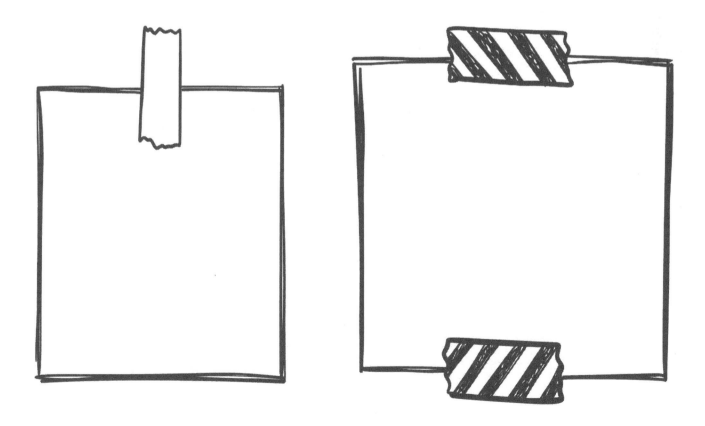

FIND TEN THINGS OUT OF PLACE

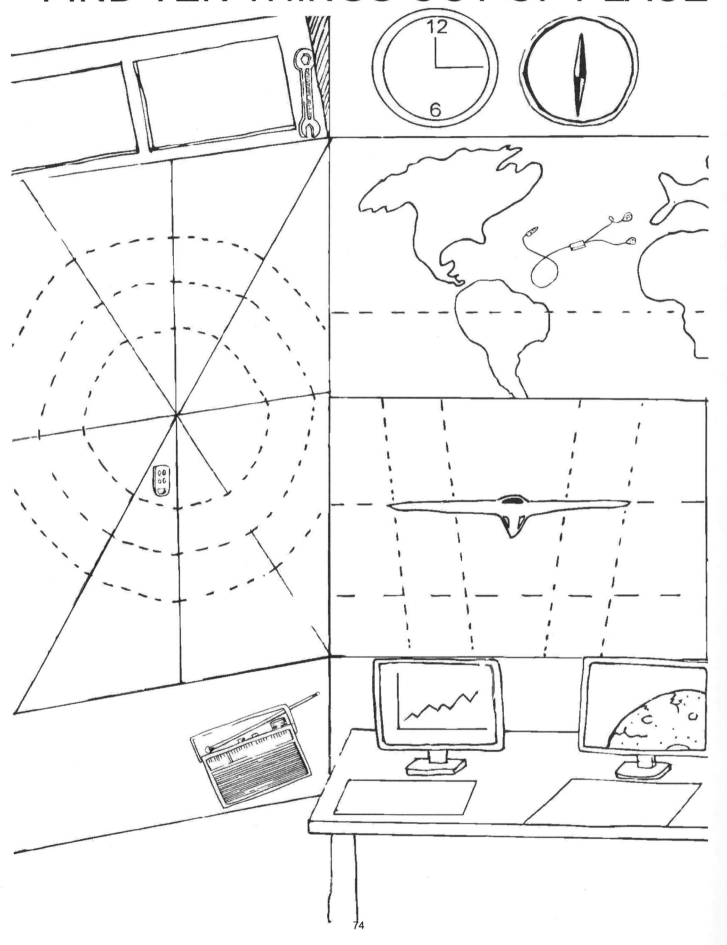

MISSION CONTROL

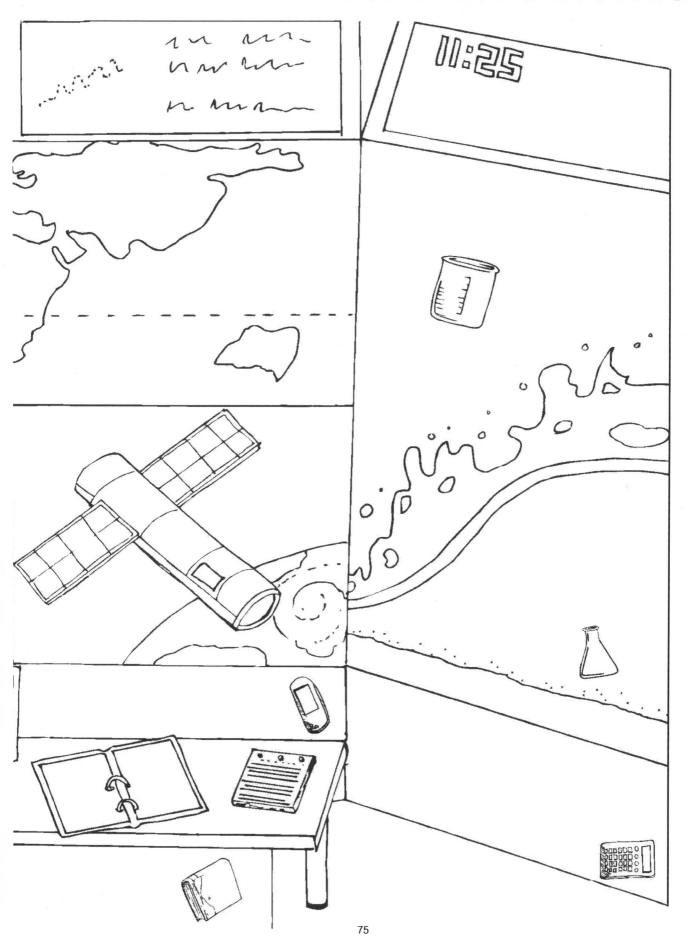

SPELLING TIME

Choose a Letter: _____

Now search your books for **20** words that
begin or end with this letter.

_____   _____
_____   _____
_____   _____
_____   _____
_____   _____
_____   _____
_____   _____
_____   _____
_____   _____
_____   _____

Use these words to create a silly story or
poem about a day in your life on Mars.

_____
_____
_____
_____
_____
_____
_____
_____
_____

AN AWESOME QUOTE:

Who Said It:

_____

Copy the Quote Here:

_____
_____
_____
_____
_____
_____
_____

IN TEN YEARS I PLAN TO...

NOTE TO FUTURE SELF:

_____
_____
_____

What is the purpose of Mars orbiters? What is an orbiter? What is a Mars helicopter?

_____

_____

_____

_____

_____

_____

_____

_____

Write down the names of three Mars orbiters that you would like to research further :

1._____

_____

2._____

_____

3._____

_____

News from Mars

Month: Day: Year:

RED PLANET TURNS GREEN

Life on the Red Planet

Month: Day: Year:

MORE ABANDONED MINES!

BE CREATIVE!

IMAGINE YOU ARE LEADING A MISSION TO MARS

How would you make sure that you and your team stays healthy during the journey?

DESIGN, INVENT, BUILD & PLAY

Use Lego, Clay, Art Supplies or Digital Art Apps to build
a model of your created environment on Mars.

What is a space agency?

Write down names of some space agencies:

_____

_____

_____

_____

_____

_____

_____

_____

Choose three missions/projects by **NASA** or **SpaceX** that you would like to research further :

1._____

_____

2._____

_____

3._____

_____

MOVIE TIME

Watch a video about space and space travel!

TITLE:_____

RATING:

Draw Your Favorite Scenes:

READING TIME

Get out all your books and read for 30 minutes.

Write & Draw about your favorite parts!

SPELLING TIME

Choose a Letter: _____

Now search your books for **20** words that
begin or end with this letter.

_____   _____
_____   _____
_____   _____
_____   _____
_____   _____
_____   _____
_____   _____
_____   _____

Use these words to create a silly story or
poem about a day in your life on Mars.

_____
_____
_____
_____
_____
_____
_____
_____

AN AWESOME QUOTE:

Who Said It:

_____

Copy the Quote Here:

_____

_____

_____

_____

_____

_____

_____

TODAY I WILL...

IN TEN YEARS I PLAN TO...

NOTE TO FUTURE SELF:

_____

_____

_____

Issue #

Only $345 Per issue!

News from Mars

Month: Day: Year:

HOUSING PODS CONSUMED BY RUST

Life on the Red Planet

Month:　　　　　　Day:　　　　　　　Year:

POLLUTION PROBLEMS? YOU BET!

CREATIVE WRITING

Continue the story:

Yasmin checked her air levels on the monitor strapped to her wrist. She found it difficult to walk across the surface of Mars in her spacesuit, but the jets that had been installed assisted her. She took a sample of the red soil before returning to the base to examine it under a microscope. Her eyes almost fell out of her head when through the lens she saw...

_____

_____

_____

_____

_____

_____

_____

_____

_____

_____

_____

_____

_____

_____

_____

_____

_____

_____

_____

_____

_____

_____

_____

_____

_____

_____

_____

_____

_____

_____

Add some artwork:

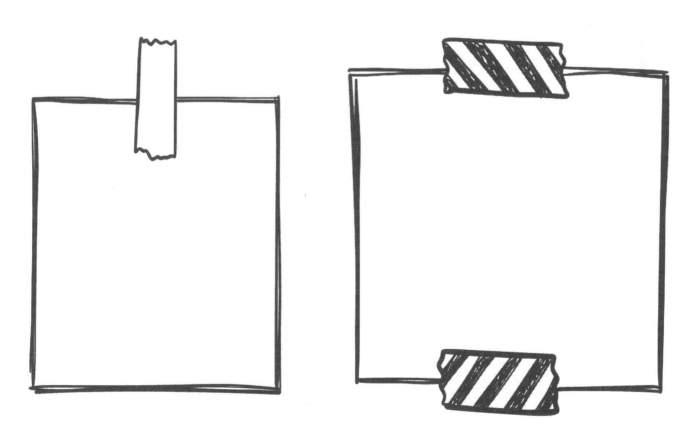

LISTENING TIME

Turn on a Podcast or News Show about Space or Technology

Notes:

_____

_____

_____

_____

_____

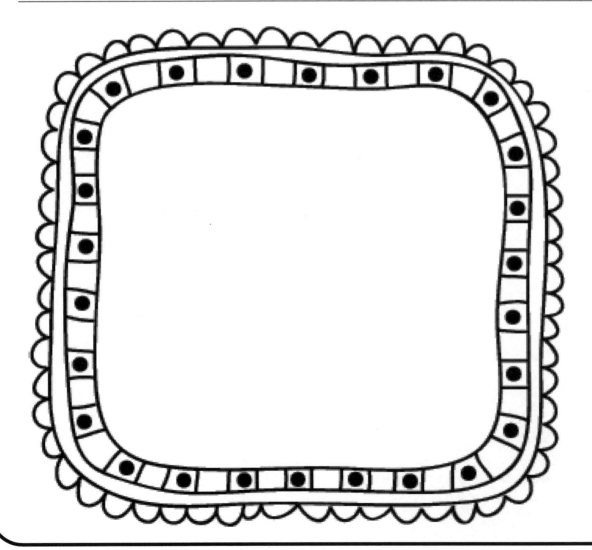

TRAVELING TO MARS

How will you spend your time? Draw your plans:

What is the terraforming of Mars?

_____

_____

_____

_____

_____

_____

_____

_____

Choose and write down three Mars terraforming challenges. Research further what are the possible ways to resolve these challenges:

1._____

_____

2._____

_____

3._____

_____

MOVIE TIME

Watch a video about space and space travel!

TITLE:_____

RATING:

READING TIME

Get out all your books and read for 30 minutes.

Write & Draw about your favorite parts!

News from Mars

Month: Day: Year:

SCIENTISTS FOCUS ON FOOD PRODUCTION

Life on the Red Planet

Month: Day: Year:

TENT CITIES POPPING UP EVERYWHERE!

SPELLING TIME

Choose a Letter: _____

Now search your books for **20** words that begin or end with this letter.

_____   _____
_____   _____
_____   _____
_____   _____
_____   _____
_____   _____
_____   _____
_____   _____
_____   _____
_____   _____

Use these words to create a silly story or poem about a day in your life on Mars.

_____
_____
_____
_____
_____
_____
_____
_____
_____

AN AWESOME QUOTE:

Who Said It:
_____

Copy the Quote Here:
_____
_____
_____
_____
_____
_____

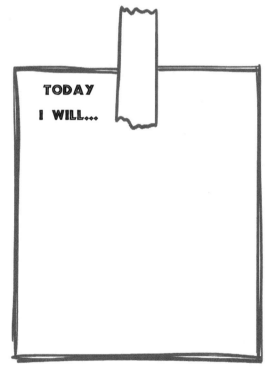

TODAY
I WILL...

NOTE TO FUTURE SELF:
_____
_____
_____

What is Mars colonization? Which space agencies are committed to researching permanent settlements on Mars?

_____

_____

_____

_____

_____

_____

_____

_____

What are some challenges of humans traveling to Mars and landing on Mars:

I._____

_____

2._____

_____

3._____

_____

CREATIVE WRITING

Continue the story:

"Chris!" Peta burst into her brother's bedroom, waving the newspaper in the air. "We won!"
She held out the article which read in big letters:
"The winners of the draw are Chris and Peta Jones! They will be taking their place on the upcoming prestigious journey to Mars!"
Weeks later, as Chris and Peta boarded the rocket excitedly, they gazed out of the round window, marveling at...

_____

_____

_____

_____

_____

_____

_____

_____

_____

_____

_____

_____

_____

_____

_____

_____

Add some artwork:

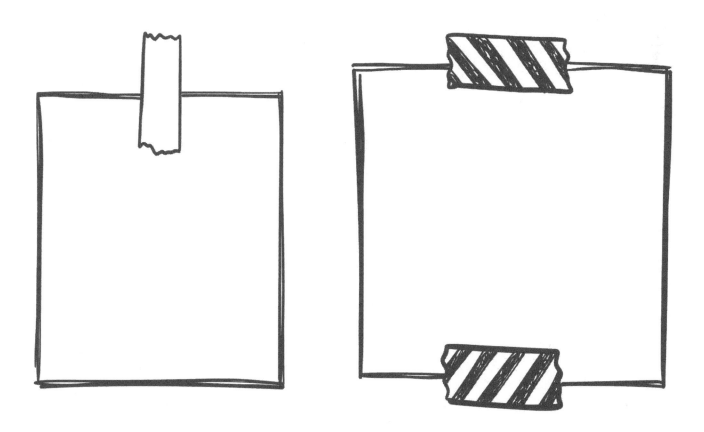

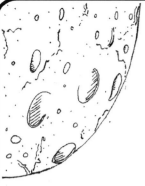

BE CREATIVE!

IMAGINE YOU ARE LEADING A MISSION TO MARS

What technology would you use to manufacture items on Mars? What kind of raw materials that are found on Mars can be used for local manufacturing?

_____

_____

_____

_____

_____

_____

_____

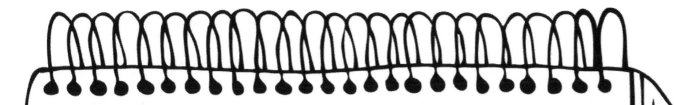

DESIGN, INVENT, BUILD & PLAY

Use Lego, Clay, Art Supplies or Digital Art Apps to build
a model of your created environment on Mars.

News from Mars

Month: Day: Year:

THE TRUTH ABOUT FARMING ON MARS

Life on the Red Planet

Month: Day: Year:

MAJOR CITIES MELTDOWN!

CREATE A COMIC STRIP

SPACE TALK

Doppler shift   Earth   eclipse

double star   earthbound   ecliptic

Drake equation   eccentricity   elliptical orbit

Look up each word. Choose the most unfamiliar word from this list and write the definition here:

_____

_____

_____

_____

_____

_____

Use this word in three sentences:

1._____

_____

2._____

_____

3._____

_____

CREATIVE WRITING

Continue the story:

Luke screwed in the last bolt before sliding out from under the jet engine. Being the chief engineer, it had taken him over a month to repair the broken rocket booster, and now he was finally done... or so he thought. He sighed in relief, tossing his wrench into the toolbox and opening the electrical panel, which revealed a complex system of multi-colored wires. But something was wrong. Luke frowned when

he realized...

_____

_____

_____

_____

_____

_____

_____

_____

_____

_____

_____

_____

_____

_____

_____

_____

Add some artwork:

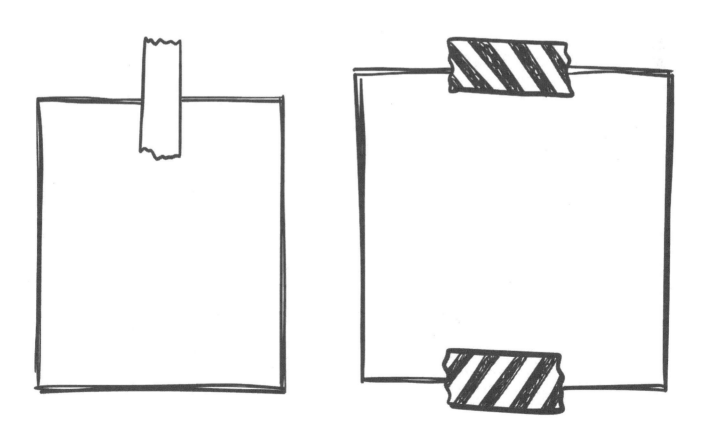

SPELLING TIME

Choose a Letter: _____

Now search your books for **20** words that
begin or end with this letter.

_____   _____
_____   _____
_____   _____
_____   _____
_____   _____
_____   _____
_____   _____
_____   _____
_____   _____
_____   _____

Use these words to create a silly story or
poem about a day in your life on Mars.

_____
_____
_____
_____
_____
_____
_____
_____

AN AWESOME QUOTE:

Who Said It:

_____

Copy the Quote Here:

_____
_____
_____
_____
_____
_____
_____

**TODAY
I WILL...**

IN TEN YEARS I PLAN TO...

NOTE TO FUTURE SELF:

_____
_____
_____

What is a Mars rover? Research crewed Mars rovers prototypes:

_____

_____

_____

_____

_____

_____

_____

_____

Choose three Mars rovers that you would like to research further:

1._____

_____

2._____

_____

3._____

_____

Issue #

Only $345 Per issue!

News from Mars

Month: Day: Year:

A COMMON MISTAKE

Life on the Red Planet

Month: Day: Year:

POWER PLANT PROBLEMS!

BE CREATIVE!
IMAGINE YOU ARE LEADING A MISSION TO MARS

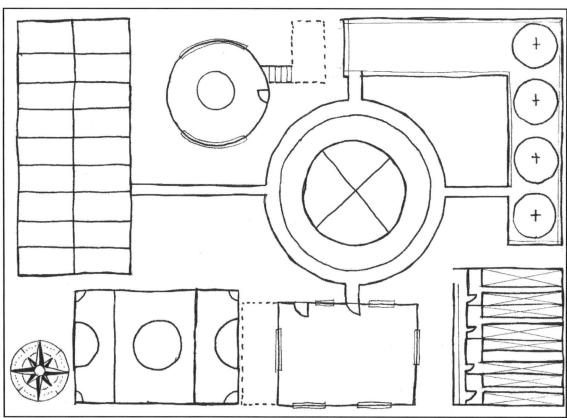

Draw a plan of your Mars colony.
What units would it include?

_____

_____

_____

_____

_____

_____

DESIGN, INVENT, BUILD & PLAY

Use Lego, Clay, Art Supplies or Digital Art Apps to build
a model of your created environment on Mars.

Research and write about the magnetic field on
Mars:

_____

_____

_____

_____

_____

_____

_____

_____

Write down three facts about Mar's atmosphere:

I._____

_____

2._____

_____

3._____

_____

CREATE A COMIC STRIP

SPACE TALK

galaxy	gegenschein	gibbous moon
gamma ray	geostationary	globular cluster
gas giant	geosynchronous	gravitation

Look up each word. Choose the most unfamiliar word from this list and write the definition here:

_____

_____

_____

_____

_____

_____

Use this word in three sentences:

1._____

_____

2._____

_____

3._____

_____

Read about astronaut life on the space station.
Write down one interesting fact about their daily
life:

_____

_____

_____

_____

_____

_____

_____

_____

Write down the names of the three astronauts who
inspire you the most.

1._____

_____

2._____

_____

3._____

_____

News from Mars

Month: Day: Year:

NEW ECO CAMP FOR SPACE TOURISTS

Life on the Red Planet

Month:　　　　　　　Day:　　　　　　　Year:

THE LONE SURVIVOR

BE CREATIVE!

IMAGINE YOU ARE LEADING A MISSION TO MARS

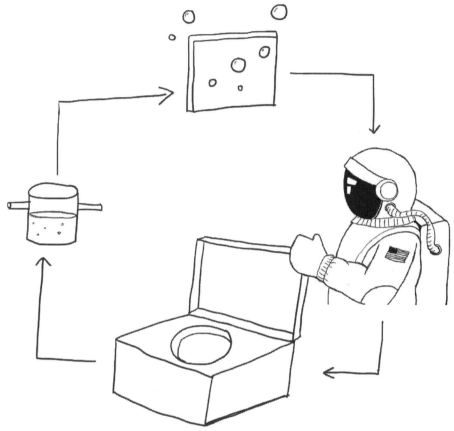

How are you going to produce oxygen to sustain the life of your colony?

_____

_____

_____

_____

_____

_____

_____

DESIGN, INVENT, BUILD & PLAY

Use Lego, Clay, Art Supplies or Digital Art Apps to build
a model of your created environment on Mars.

SPELLING TIME

Choose a Letter: _____

Now search your books for **20** words that
begin or end with this letter.

_____   _____
_____   _____
_____   _____
_____   _____
_____   _____
_____   _____
_____   _____
_____   _____

Use these words to create a silly story or
poem about a day in your life on Mars.

_____
_____
_____
_____
_____
_____
_____
_____

AN AWESOME QUOTE:

Who Said It:

_____

Copy the Quote Here:

_____
_____
_____
_____
_____
_____
_____

TODAY
I WILL...

NOTE TO FUTURE SELF:

_____
_____
_____

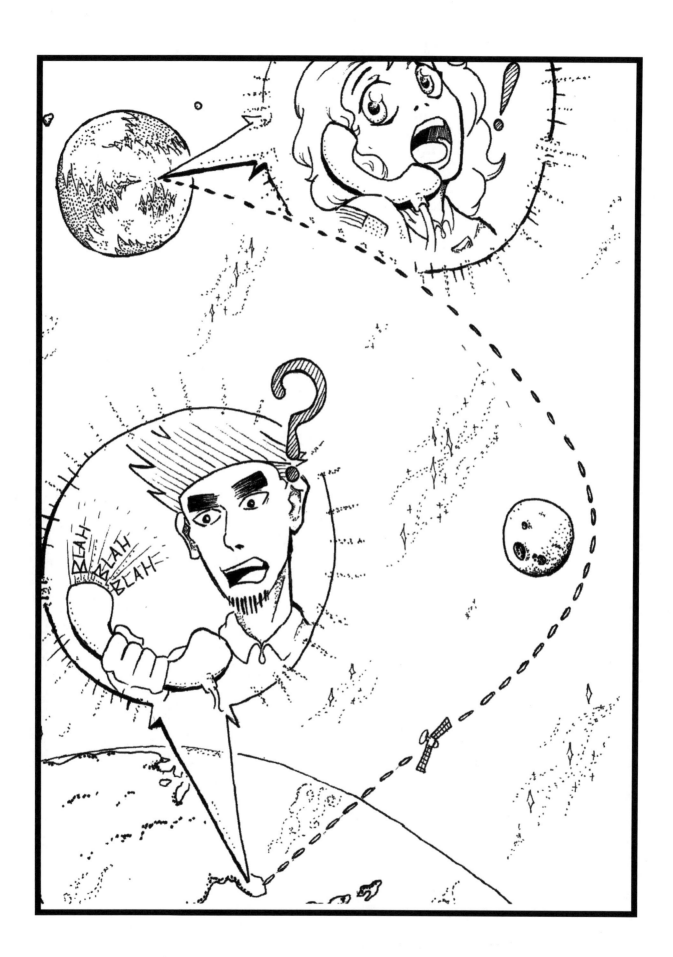

What types of antennas and radio waves are used
for Earth-to-spacecraft communication?

_____

_____

_____

_____

_____

_____

_____

_____

What are some challenges for direct communication
between Earth and Mars:

1._____

_____

2._____

_____

3._____

_____

CREATIVE WRITING

Continue the story:

"Is the specimen properly contained?" Dr. Holloway asked Levi.

"Affirmative," Levi nodded. "Though its appetite is unbelievable. It's eaten a week's supply of food in the past hour."

"I'll get on that," Dr. Holloway nodded, checking her watch. She traveled through the Mars base to Storage Unit 214 to retrieve a few boxes of rations. On her way back to the containment facility, she got a fright when Levi burst out of Room 339, covered in icky slime.

"What happened?" Dr Holloway gasped.

"Well," Levi chuckled nervously, "It's a funny story."

_____

_____

_____

_____

_____

_____

_____

_____

_____

_____

_____

_____

_____

_____

_____

_____

_____

Add some artwork:

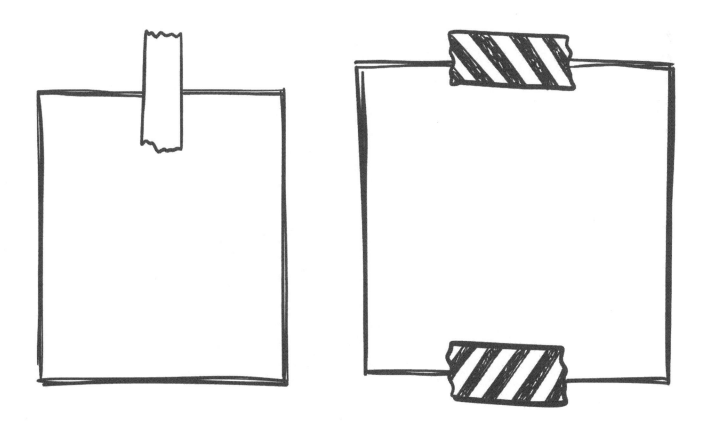

News from Mars

Month: **Day:**   **Year:**

BORN IN SPACE

Life on the Red Planet

Month: Day: Year:

GRANDFATHERS LIVING THE DREAM

CREATIVE WRITING

Continue the story:

Tori couldn't wait. For four long years she and her crew had lived in a temporary base on the Red Planet, and though it had been such an amazing experience, she couldn't wait to return to beloved Earth. Final safety checks had been made and their lift-off was flawless. As the ship drifted away towards home, she sighed, having never really gotten used to the sheer beauty of Mars. But her eyes suddenly widened as she stood up and cried, "Oh no! We've forgotten the..."

_____

_____

_____

_____

_____

_____

_____

_____

_____

_____

_____

_____

_____

_____

_____

_____

_____

_____
_____
_____
_____
_____
_____
_____
_____
_____
_____
_____
_____
_____

Add some artwork:

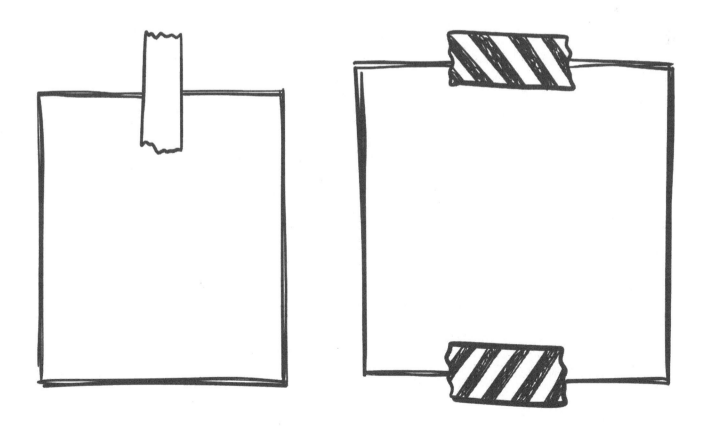

What is an effect of a low gravity and no-gravity environment on a human body? What is gravity on Mars?

_____

_____

_____

_____

_____

_____

_____

_____

Write three ideas on how dwellers of a Mars settlement can adjust their life to Mars' environment :

I._____

_____

2._____

_____

3._____

_____

SPELLING TIME

Choose a Letter: _____

Now search your books for **20** words that
begin or end with this letter.

_____   _____
_____   _____
_____   _____
_____   _____
_____   _____
_____   _____
_____   _____
_____   _____
_____   _____
_____   _____

Use these words to create a silly story or
poem about a day in your life on Mars.

_____
_____
_____
_____
_____
_____
_____
_____

AN AWESOME QUOTE:

Who Said It:

_____

Copy the Quote Here:

_____
_____
_____
_____
_____
_____

**TODAY
I WILL...**

IN TEN YEARS I PLAN TO...

NOTE TO FUTURE SELF:

_____
_____
_____

CREATE A COMIC STRIP

SPACE TALK

hydrogen	inclination	interstellar
hyperbolic orbit	inertia	interstellar dust
hypernova	inferior planets	ionosphere

Look up each word. Choose the most unfamiliar word from this list and write the definition here:

_____

_____

_____

_____

_____

_____

Use this word in three sentences:

1._____

_____

2._____

_____

3._____

_____

News from Mars

Month: Day: Year:

WHEN CHILDREN VENTURE OUTSIDE

Life on the Red Planet

Month: Day: Year:

A NEW CITY RISES FROM THE DIRT

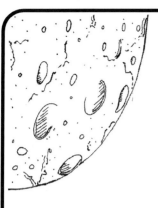

BE CREATIVE!

IMAGINE YOU ARE LEADING A MISSION TO MARS

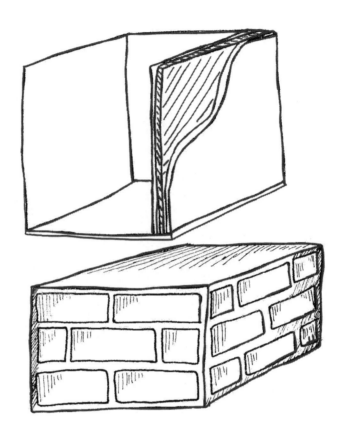

What materials would you use for construction of your colony?

_____

_____

_____

_____

_____

_____

_____

DESIGN, INVENT, BUILD & PLAY

Use Lego, Clay, Art Supplies or Digital Art Apps to build
a model of your created environment on Mars.

MOVIE TIME

Watch a video about space and space travel!

TITLE:_____

RATING:

Draw Your Favorite Scenes:

READING TIME

Get out all your books and read for 30 minutes.

Write & Draw about your favorite parts!

Why is water so important for Mars colonization?

_____

_____

_____

_____

_____

_____

_____

Write down some forms of water or names of water
bodies that are found on Mars:

1._____

_____

2._____

_____

3._____

_____

LISTENING TIME

Turn on a Podcast or News Show about Space or Technology

Notes:

_____
_____
_____
_____
_____
_____

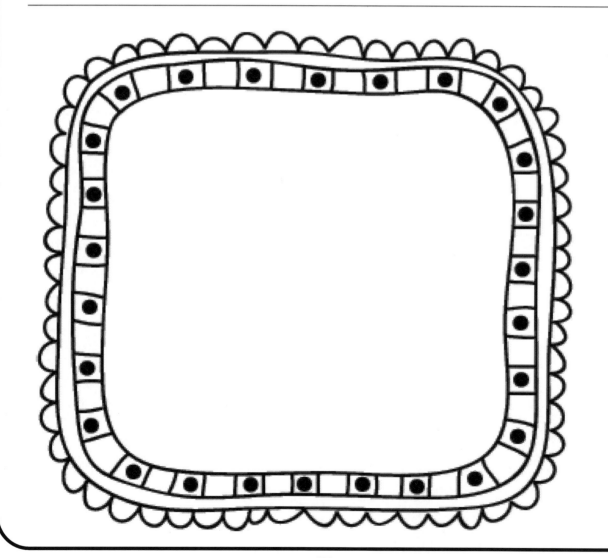

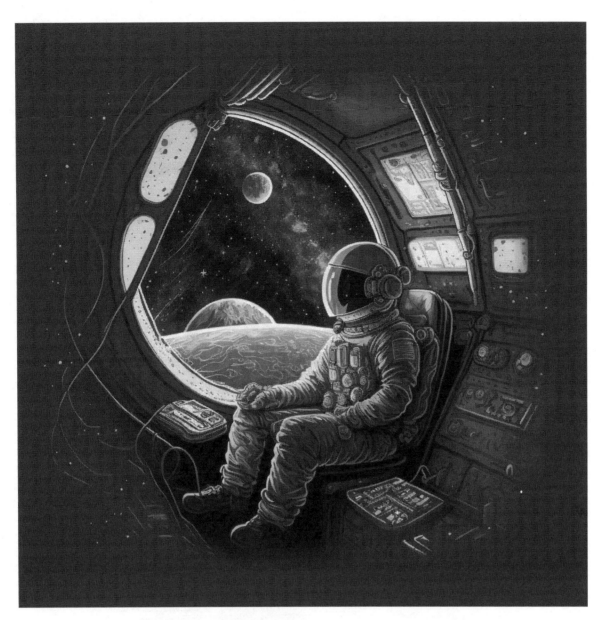

TRAVELING TO MARS

How will you spend your time? Draw your plans:

News from Mars

Month: Day: Year:

BASKETBALL PLAYERS DEFY GRAVITY!

Life on the Red Planet

Month:　　　　　　　Day:　　　　　　　Year:

"THE SKY IS FALLING!"
DON'T PANIC, DOME CRACKING IS NORMAL!

 # CREATIVE WRITING

Continue the story:

"Good evening Ladies and Gentlemen. I am here today to outline the events that took place on June 29th 2053, following Astro X VI 's landing on the Red Planet. I know there have been many speculations and I am here today to set the record straight about this mission.

Firstly, I am pleased to inform you that the mission was a relative success, however... "

_____

_____

_____

_____

_____

_____

_____

_____

_____

_____

_____

_____

_____

_____

_____

_____

_____

_____

_____

_____

_____

_____

_____

_____

_____

_____

_____

_____

_____

_____

_____

Add some artwork:

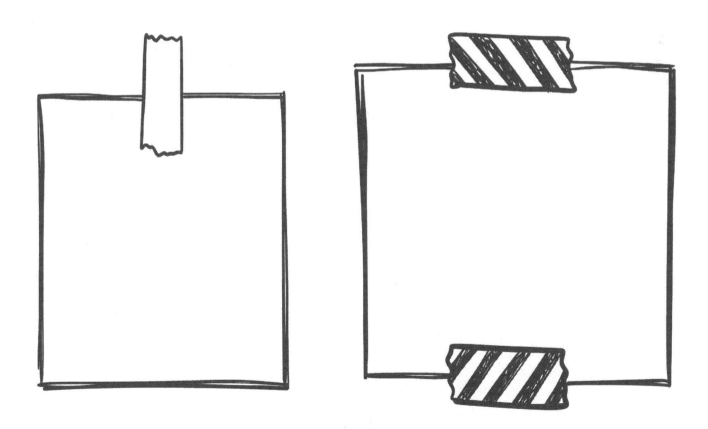

What is aerogel?

_____

_____

_____

_____

_____

_____

_____

_____

Write down names of three modern inventions or technologies that can be used for building a settlement on Mars. Research them further.

1._____

_____

2._____

_____

3._____

_____

BE CREATIVE!

IMAGINE YOU ARE LEADING A MISSION TO MARS

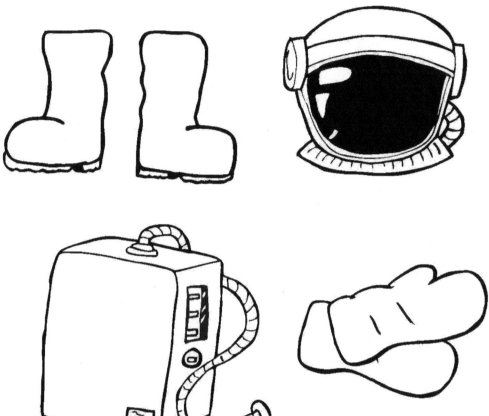

What kind of spacesuit would you choose for yourself?

_____

_____

_____

_____

_____

_____

_____

DESIGN, INVENT, BUILD & PLAY

Use Lego, Clay, Art Supplies or Digital Art Apps to build
a model of your created environment on Mars.

CREATE A COMIC STRIP

SPACE TALK

kiloparsec	Lagrange points	magnitude
Kirkwood gaps	light-year	meteor
Kuiper belt	local group	meteorite

Look up each word. Choose the most unfamiliar word from this list and write the definition here:

_____

_____

_____

_____

_____

_____

Use this word in three sentences:

1._____

_____

2._____

_____

3._____

_____

TITLE:

News from Mars

Month: Day: Year:

DRONE HOMES HOVERING ABOVE

Life on the Red Planet

Month: Day: Year:

EXCITING NEW TECHNOLOGIES!

What is needed to grow food on Mars?

_____

_____

_____

_____

_____

_____

_____

_____

What in your opinion would be the best food to grow in Mars settlement?

1._____

_____

2._____

_____

3._____

_____

BE CREATIVE!

IMAGINE YOU ARE LEADING A MISSION TO MARS

What equipment would you like to bring with you
for exploration of the planet?

_____

_____

_____

_____

_____

_____

_____

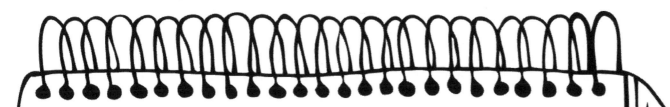

DESIGN, INVENT, BUILD & PLAY

Use Lego, Clay, Art Supplies or Digital Art Apps to build
a model of your created environment on Mars.

MOVIE TIME

Watch a video about space and space travel!

TITLE:_____

RATING:

Draw Your Favorite Scenes:

READING
TIME

Get out all your books and read for 30 minutes.

Write & Draw about your favorite parts!

CREATE A COMIC STRIP

SPACE TALK

radiation	telemetry	visual magnitude
Roche limit	telescope	waning
scintillation	terminator	waxing
spectroscope	terrestrial	weightlessness
synodic	variable star	wormhole
syzygy	vernal equinox	zenith

Look up each word. Choose the most unfamiliar word from this list and write the definition here:

_____

_____

_____

_____

Use this word in three sentences:

1._____

_____

2._____

_____

3._____

_____

TITLE:

News from Mars

Month: Day: Year:

THE SCIENCE OF FARMING ON MARS

Life on the Red Planet

Month: Day: Year:

HOMELESS FAMILIES SEEK SHELTER

What would settlers need to learn and practice before they travel to Mars?

_____

_____

_____

_____

_____

_____

_____

_____

_____

What professionals would be most needed on crew of Mars settlement?

1._____

_____

2._____

_____

3._____

_____

LISTENING TIME

Turn on a Podcast or News Show about Space or Technology

Notes:

_____

_____

_____

_____

_____

_____

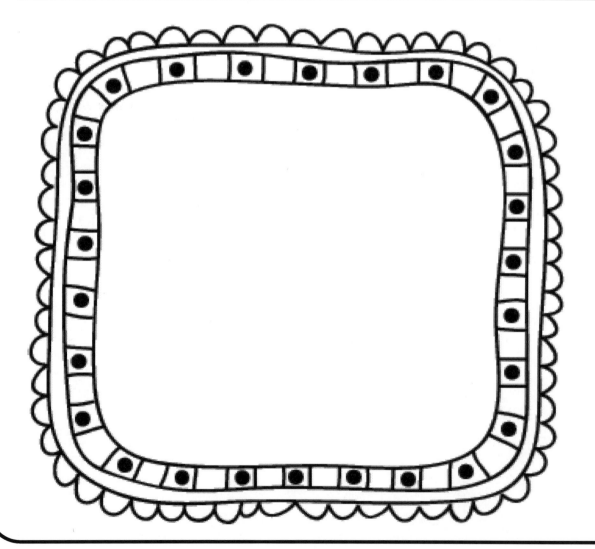

TRAVELING TO MARS

How will you spend your time? Draw your plans:

CREATIVE WRITING

Continue the story:

Day 249. Dear Diary. We have been here for many months now. Although I am so honored to have been chosen for this mission, I miss home very much. The differences between Mars and Earth continue to blow me away. I have yet to find any real similarities. For example..."

_____

_____

_____

_____

_____

_____

_____

_____

_____

_____

_____

_____

_____

_____

_____

_____

Add some artwork:

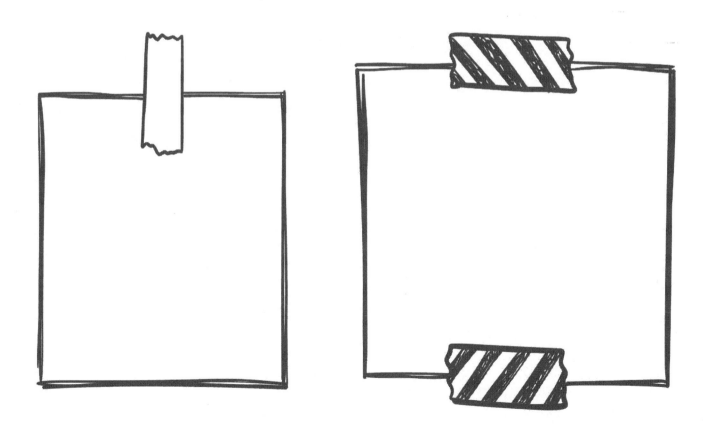

MOVIE TIME

Watch a video about space and space travel!

TITLE:_____

Draw Your Favorite Scenes:

RATING:

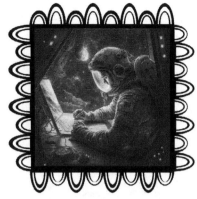

READING TIME

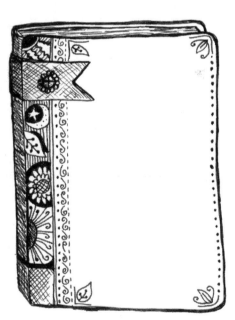

Write and draw about what you are reading.

News from Mars

Month: Day: Year:

LET'S GO FISHING!

Life on the Red Planet

Month: Day: Year:

THE TREES CAN BREATHE! WHY CAN'T WE?

DIY

BONUS PAGES

News from Mars

Month: Day: Year:

Life on the Red Planet

Month: Day: Year:

Issue #

Only $345 Per issue!

News from Mars

Month: Day: Year:

Life on the Red Planet

Month: Day: Year:

News from Mars

Month: Day: Year:

Life on the Red Planet

Month: Day: Year:

TITLE:

TITLE:

TITLE:

TITLE:

_____

_____

_____

_____

_____

_____

_____

_____

_____

_____

TITLE:

TITLE:

TITLE:

TITLE:

TITLE:

TITLE:

TITLE:

TITLE:

TITLE:

DESIGN A SETTLEMENT

DESIGN A SCHOOL

DESIGN A RESTAURANT

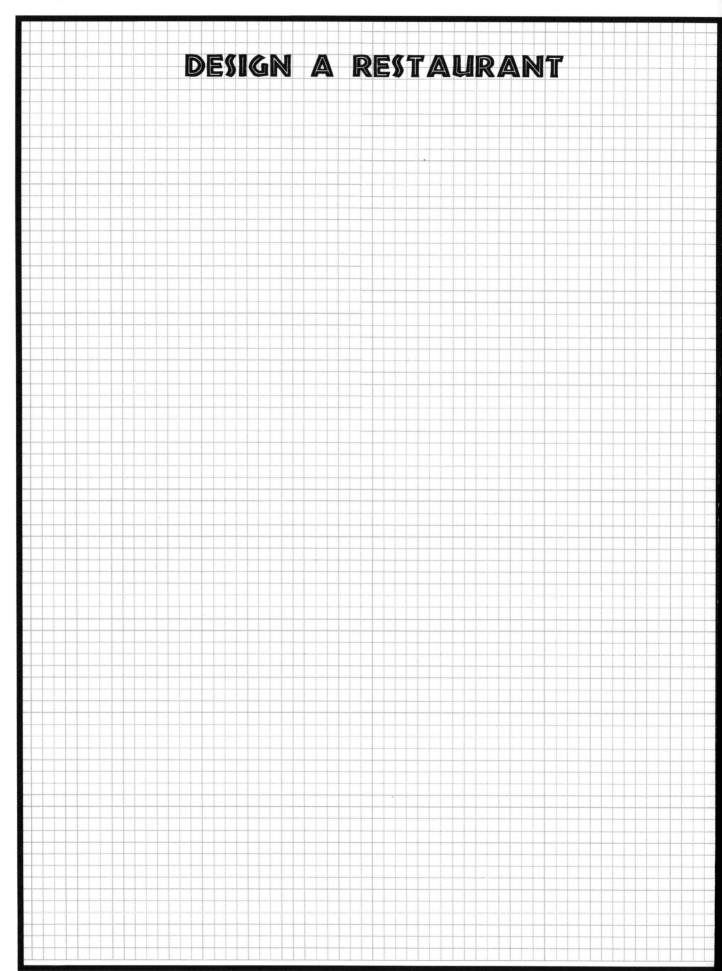

DESIGN AN ENTERTAINMENT CENTER

DESIGN A GREEN HOUSE

DESIGN A HOME

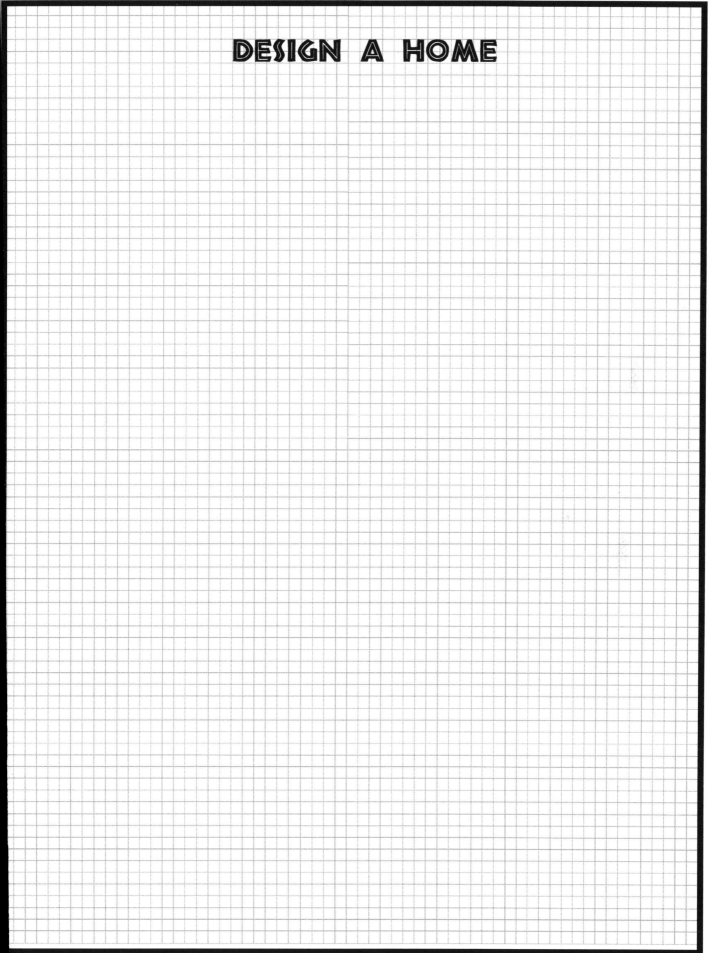

ABOUT THE AUTHOR
Sarah Janisse Brown

I spent my childhood in Titusville, Florida across the river from the Space Center at Cape Canaveral. Our family calendar revolved around art festivals and Space Shuttle launches. My mom was an artist and My dad worked at the Space Center in the 1980's.

We would feel the rumble and would run out into the front yard and into the street to watch the launch. My dad knew exactly when the launches were going to happen, and he would prep us for the count down, he was often one of the last to leave the launch pad before take off. Ten. Nine. Eight. Seven... this is how I learned to count backwards when I was four years old.

My dad worked with NASA when I was a little girl, and often took me to the Space Center. We never missed a launch. I was there when the Challenger exploded, looking into the sky.

Space Exploration was a very normal part of my childhood, but I knew it was special. When I was 12 I was certain that I would be an astronaut or aerospace engineer, or maybe I was going to be a Space Camp Director.

This is my dad's Space hat, he got a new button for every launch he participated in.

Here's a picture of me and my inheritance- a tile from the Columbia that my dad removed and was redesigning after the shuttle returned from its orbit.

MISSION TO MARS

RESEARCH, IMAGINE, EXPLORE & PLAN YOUR ADVENTURE

Fun-Schooling With Thinking Tree Books

Copyright Information FunSchooling.com

Made in the USA
Las Vegas, NV
15 March 2023

69161447R00133